Contents

DID YOU KNOW?

Discover amazing facts about ants.

HUMAN INTERACTION

Find out what happens when humans and ants come into contact with each other.

Some words are shown in bold, **like this**. You can find out what they mean by looking in the glossary.

HABITAT IN DANGER

Learn how some ants' habitats are under threat, and what is being done to protect them.

Welcome to the colony!

Ants are amazing animals. They're tiny – less than a millionth of the size of a human being. But they're extremely strong, with superhuman senses and great communication skills. They can share tasks, work together in a team, and pass on complicated messages. Scientists still aren't sure how they manage some of their incredible feats!

What is an ant?

An ant is a type of insect. Like all insects, ants have three main body parts, six legs, and a pair of **antennae**, or feelers. Scientists have discovered around 12,500 ant **species**, ranging in size from about 1 millimetre (0.04 inches) to 5 centimetres (2 inches) long.

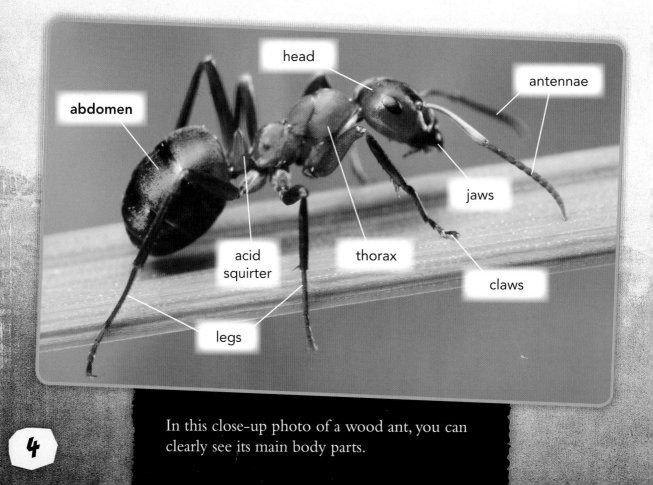

head

antennae

abdomen

jaws

acid squirter

thorax

claws

legs

In this close-up photo of a wood ant, you can clearly see its main body parts.

A Colony of Ants

and Other Insect Groups

Anna Claybourne

www.raintreepublishers.co.uk
Visit our website to find out more information about Raintree books.

To order:
☎ Phone 0845 6044371
🖷 Fax +44 (0) 1865 312263
🖳 Email myorders@raintreepublishers.co.uk

Customers from outside the UK please telephone +44 1865 312262

Raintree is an imprint of Capstone Global Library Limited, a company incorporated in England and Wales having its registered office at 7 Pilgrim Street, London, EC4V 6LB – Registered company number: 6695582

Text © Capstone Global Library Limited 2013
First published in hardback in 2013
Paperback edition first published in 2014
The moral rights of the proprietor have been asserted.

Edited by Nancy Dickmann, Adam Miller, and Laura Knowles
Designed by Richard Parker
Picture research by Ruth Blair
Original Illustrations © Capstone Global Library Ltd 2013
Illustrations by Jeff Edwards
Originated by Capstone Global Library Ltd
Printed and bound in China by CTPS

ISBN 978 1 406 23946 1 (hardback)
16 15 14 13 12
10 9 8 7 6 5 4 3 2 1

ISBN 978 1 406 23953 9 (paperback)
17 16 15 14 13
10 9 8 7 6 5 4 3 2 1

British Library Cataloguing in Publication Data
Claybourne, Anna.
A colony of ants and other insect groups.
-- (Animals in groups)
595.7'156-dc22
A full catalogue record for this book is available from the British Library.

Acknowledgements
We would like to thank the following for permission to reproduce photographs: Alamy pp. 22 (© blickwinkel, 33 (© neil setchfield yuckfood.com); Corbis pp. 13 (© Alex Wild/Visuals Unlimited), 27 (© Michael & Patricia Fogden); Dreamstime.com p. 26 (© Gordon Miller); iStockphoto pp. 15 (© Henrik Larsson), 25 (© Focus_on_Nature); Naturepl pp. 9 (© Nature Production), 21 (© Mark Bowler), 23 (© Bence Mate), 30 (© Visuals Unlimited), 31 (© Meul / ARCO); Science Photo Library pp. 17 (NATURE'S IMAGES), 19 (MONA LISA PRODUCTION/), 39 (SALLY BENSUSEN), 41 (PASCAL GOETGHELUCK); Shutterstock pp. 4 (© Andrey Pavlov), 5, 8, 18 (© Christopher Tan Teck Hean), 7 (© xfox01), 11 (© AlexGul), 12 (© Falk Kienas), 16 (© Juha Sompinmäki), 28, 32 (© Henrik Larsson), 35 (© vblinov), 36 (© Daniel Prudek), 37 (© Ratikova).

Cover photograph of leafcutter ants reproduced with permission of Alamy (© Picture Press).

Every effort has been made to contact copyright holders of any material reproduced in this book. Any omissions will be rectified in subsequent printings if notice is given to the publisher.

Disclaimer
All the Internet addresses (URLs) given in this book were valid at the time of going to press. However, due to the dynamic nature of the Internet, some addresses may have changed, or sites may have changed or ceased to exist since publication. While the author and publisher regret any inconvenience this may cause readers, no responsibility for any such changes can be accepted by either the author or the publisher.

HUMAN INTERACTION

Ants can be a nuisance for humans. They often steal our food and invade our homes. For every human being on Earth, scientists think there are up to a million ants.

Ants are "social insects". They live together in big groups, called **colonies**, and share the jobs they need to do to survive. They take turns at tasks such as finding food, digging tunnels, or guarding the nest. One ant, the queen, lays eggs for the colony, and the others look after the babies. A colony can have the same population of ants as humans in a big city!

These ants are working together to carry a piece of food back to their nest.

DID YOU KNOW?

Driver ants (also called safari ants) have enormous colonies. One colony can contain more than 20 million ants!

Why do ants live together?

Living in a group makes sense for ants. Sharing a nest and food protects them from danger and starvation, much better than if they lived alone.

Ants will fight to defend other members of their colony. An individual ant may even die fighting to protect the others. That's not very good news for that ant, of course! But it does mean that each ant has thousands of others looking out for it. Baby ants and the queen are especially well protected. This makes sure that the colony can keep going, even if it is attacked.

Not just ants

It's not only ants that live in big groups – some other insects such as bees, wasps, and termites do, too. So do humans, in a way. You don't have to grow all your own food or write your own schoolbooks! Instead, each person has their own job to do, and people do things for each other.

DID YOU KNOW?

Some scientists think that an ant colony works almost like one "super-**organism**". It's like a giant creature, made up of many tiny, separate parts. Some even compare an ant colony to a human brain. Ants don't think about their decisions in the same way that people do, but a whole ant colony together can have a similar number of brain cells to one human brain.

To us, ants may look as if they are running around randomly, but they are all busy doing jobs, communicating and helping each other.

7

Different shapes

In each ant species, there are several different types of ant, known as **castes**. Each caste has its own role to play in the colony. The castes are often different sizes, and may also look different.

Who's who?

Ant castes include queens, males, and worker ants. In a typical colony, there are lots of workers, but just one queen and a few males.

The queen is an egg machine. Although she's called the queen, she doesn't really rule the colony. She just lays eggs, which the workers carry away and care for.

These forest ants are both the same species, and both worker ants. But the bigger one is a soldier, while the other is a normal worker.

These "honeypot" ants are holding a store of honeydew for their colony.

A male ant's job is to leave the nest and **mate** with a new queen, so that new colonies can start. Only a few male ants are born in a colony each year. As they have to search far and wide for a mate, they have wings.

Worker ants are the "normal" ants you see scurrying around. They are all female. There can be several different sizes of worker ant in a colony, and some may also have special features. Soldier ants are workers with extra-large jaws, for fighting enemies. In some species, a few workers are used as storage jars! Other workers feed them a food called **honeydew** (see page 26) and they swell up to the size of grapes. They hang from a tunnel roof deep in the nest, until the food is needed. They can pass it back out through their mouths to the other ants.

Ants are everywhere

Wherever you live in the world, you're probably no stranger to ants. They are found almost everywhere on our planet, except in the deep oceans and the freezing polar regions.

Scientists think ants have existed for around 150 million years. Over time, they have spread out across most of the world, and developed into thousands of different species. Ants are super-survivors, and have adapted, or changed, to suit all kinds of different **habitats**.

HABITAT IN DANGER

A few ant species are **endangered** because of damage to their habitats. The Sri Lankan relict ant is one. It is at risk because its forest habitat in Sri Lanka has been cleared and broken up.

The Sahara Desert ant lives in burrows in the desert sand, and can come out to search for food even in temperatures above 50 degrees Celsius (122 degrees Fahrenheit). That is hotter than a very hot bath! This ant is one of the most heat-resistant animals on Earth. Its body makes **chemicals** that prevent it from becoming too hot.

One type of ant, the beachcomber ant, is adapted to survive underwater. It digs underground nests in the seaside mud, and when the tide comes in, the nests get flooded. The ants survive by trapping pockets of air in their nest chambers. They can also swim and "skate" on the water surface.

These desert ants are braving the heat of the Sun to leave their nest and search for food.

A place to live

As they work together to build their nests, ants create some of the most amazing animal homes in the world. They can have thousands of connected tunnels and neatly arranged chambers.

A typical ant home is an underground nest in the soil or sand. The ants dig out the underground tunnels and rooms, and carry all the dirt they remove up to the surface. This makes an anthill – a heap of sand or soil that forms the upper part of the nest.

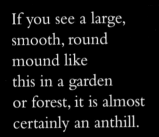

If you see a large, smooth, round mound like this in a garden or forest, it is almost certainly an anthill.

DID YOU KNOW?

In Brazil in 2004, scientists filled an empty leafcutter ants' nest with concrete, then cleared away the soil around it. They found it reached 8 metres (26 feet) underground and contained more than 7,000 chambers.

Unusual nests

Some species have other ways of making a home. Here are a few of them:

- Weaver ants glue living leaves together in trees, using silk from an ant **larva** (baby).
- Some army ants are **nomadic**, which means they move from place to place, and have no fixed home. Sometimes, they all clump together and form a cosy nest made from their own bodies!
- Some ant colonies live inside "ant plants", such as myrmecodias. These plants have a swollen base full of hollow tunnels where ants can live. In return, the ants' droppings provide the plant with **nutrients** that help them grow.

These Argentine ants are scurrying along the tunnels in their nest.

How do ants communicate?

Ants living together in a colony have to be able to communicate. The main way they do this is by using special chemicals (substances) that they release from their bodies.

An ant's body can release many different message chemicals, known as **pheromones**. Each one has its own scent, or smell. Other ants pick up the scent using their antennae.

How do they do it?

Ants have special body parts, called glands, that make pheromones. Some are in the head or antennae, some in the abdomen, and some, such as the poison gland, are in the tail. The glands make the pheromones and release them on to the ant's body surface. The pheromones can escape into the air, or rub off on to the ground to leave a chemical trail.

An ant uses its ultra-sensitive antennae to spot different pheromones. They send the sense signals to the ant's brain, so that it gets the message. Ants wave their antennae in the air, use them to track a trail along the ground, or touch other ants to pick up signals. They can also taste food with them. The antennae sense is a bit like our senses of taste and smell combined.

DID YOU KNOW?

Ants cannot see very well. Most species have poor eyesight, and in some species, the workers are completely blind.

Unlike most other insects, an ant's antennae are "elbowed", meaning they have joints in the middle. This helps ants position their antennae and move them around more easily.

What do ants say?

Ants send many different kinds of chemical messages. Here are some of them:

- *This way to the food!:* Ants show the way to a good source of food using a chemical trail along the ground.

- *I'm your friend:* Ants can tell which other ants belong to their own colony by their pheromones.

- *The queen is safe:* The queen constantly makes pheromones to let all the other ants know that she's alive and laying eggs.

- *This is my job:* Each ant releases chemicals to tell others its role, such as baby-feeder or nest-builder.

You can often see ants following a pheromone trail to and fro between a food source.

A bullet ant checks out a beetle to see whether it poses a threat to the ant colony.

- *No food here:* If a food source has run out, or a pathway leads to a dead end, a pheromone can tell other ants not to bother going that way.

- *Danger alert!:* An alarm pheromone warns other ants of a threat, and asks for help.

- *Hey, get off me!:* If an ant is attacked by enemy ants, it will release strong-smelling pheromones to warn them off.

DID YOU KNOW?

Some ants use pheromones to trick other ants. When invading another colony, they can copy their enemies' pheromone and pretend to belong to the nest to avoid attack. Or they release "propaganda pheromones" that confuse their enemies, making them attack each other instead of the invaders.

Ant eyes

While some ants are blind, many do have eyes. A typical ant has two large **compound eyes**, made of lots of small sections. It also has three much smaller eyes on the top of its head, called **ocelli**. The compound eyes are better at seeing, and ants can use them to spot landmarks and food. The ocelli can detect light and dark, and the position of the Sun, but cannot see clearly.

Getting in touch

Ants use their antennae to detect chemical messages, but they also use them to touch and stroke each other. This helps to spread chemical signals around the colony. Scientists think it may be used to pass on other messages, too.

Two ants meet on a rose to rub their antennae together and "kiss", or exchange food and chemical messages with their mouths.

A scientist watches as ants choose pathways through a set of mazes to learn more about how they communicate.

Feel the vibrations

Ants can also use sounds to communicate, though they do not "speak" using their mouths. Instead they rub sections of their abdomens together to make sounds called stridulations. The other ants can "hear" the sounds by sensing the vibrations through the ground. Stridulations can be used as an alarm call, a distress call when one ant needs help, or to call workers together.

DID YOU KNOW?

In experiments, scientists have found that an ant can work out how to get through a maze. It can then pass this information on to another ant. Some species of ants seem to do this by touching their antennae together.

What does an ant colony eat?

Some ants eat plants, while others hunt insects or small animals, or eat carrion (animals that are already dead). Other ant foods include **fungi**, plant juice or sap, **nectar** from inside flowers, food from our kitchens, and even other ants and their eggs. Many ants are omnivores. This means they will eat almost anything.

Munching mouthparts

Ants have two pairs of jaws. The **mandibles** are the bigger pair, and are an ant's main tools. It uses them for grabbing, slicing, and carrying food. Ants use a smaller pair of jaws to chew their food.

The mandibles have other jobs as well – some ants use them for holding on to each other, fighting, or biting to defend themselves. One type of ant, the trap-jaw ant, can shut its jaws incredibly fast. When threatened, it snaps its jaws against the ground, making it spring up into the air and out of danger.

Save it for later

Ants don't just eat the food they find straight away. Instead, they carry food back to their nest, to store, share, or feed to their young. Ants can carry a lot of food at once. In some species, one ant can carry 50 times its own weight!

HABITAT IN DANGER

One type of leafcutter ant from Brazil is becoming endangered. The forests where it lives are being cut down, making it harder for the ants to collect the leaves they use for food.

Ants can slice up their food into small pieces using their mandibles.

Scout on the lookout

The ants in a colony work together to collect food. They don't all run everywhere at once, looking for food wherever they can find it. Instead, to save time and energy, "scout" ants go out first. They mainly use their antennae to sniff out food sources.

When a scout has found some food, it lays a pheromone trail, showing the other ants where to go. Soon, hundreds or thousands of ants start trekking to the food and taking it back to the nest, bit by bit. As they go, they all leave pheromones too, making the trail stronger.

Two wood ant workers feed a larger queen ant (the one with wings), by passing her food from their own mouths.

Taste this!

Ants often put their mouths together to pass food to each other. This is sometimes called "kissing", though it isn't really kissing. Ants do it to share food with other colony members, and to show other ants what kind of food they have found. It's also a good way to pass on message pheromones, which are mixed in with the food.

Leafcutter ants use their jaws to cut sections of leaves from plants, then carry the pieces up in the air as they march home along their trail.

DID YOU KNOW?

Leafcutter ants follow long trails up trees or into fields to cut off pieces of leaf, which they carry home to their nests. They don't eat the leaves, but chop them into smaller and smaller pieces, and use them to grow a special fungus that they use as food.

Going hunting

By hunting together, meat-eating ants can catch and kill animals much bigger than themselves. Usually, they catch other insects, such as grasshoppers or flies, or sometimes worms. But some ants can catch birds or snakes.

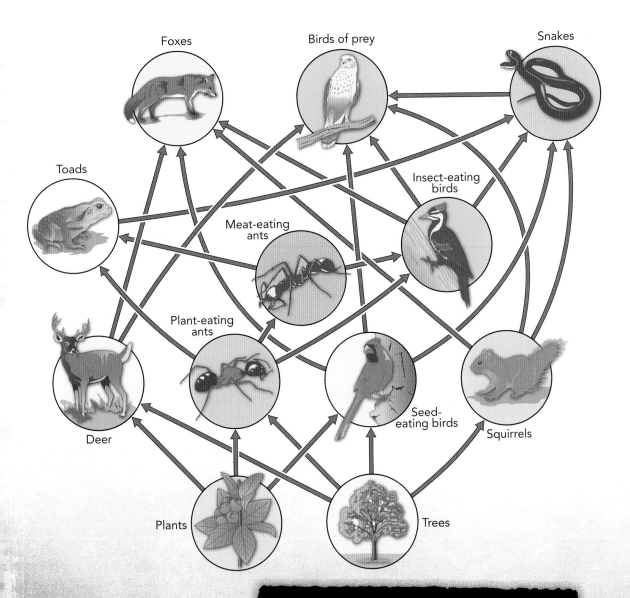

Foxes

Birds of prey

Snakes

Toads

Insect-eating birds

Meat-eating ants

Plant-eating ants

Seed-eating birds

Squirrels

Deer

Plants

Trees

Ants play a big part in many food webs, including this woodland web. Arrows point from each living thing to an animal that eats it.

To kill **prey**, the ants surround their victim, drag it down, and bite or sting it. Then they work in a team to carry it back to the nest. If it's too big, they use their mandibles to cut it into smaller pieces.

In some ants, the mandibles are big and strong. If a trap-jaw ant bit you, it would hurt a lot. In other ants, the sting is the main weapon. Fire ants get their name from their burning stings. The bullet ant has the worst insect sting in the world – the terrible pain goes on for 24 hours!

An anteater uses its long tongue to fish ants out of their nests.

Ants and ecosystems

Ants play an important part in the **ecosystem** wherever they live. They carry away rotting, dead creatures, and dig in the soil, making it easier for plants to grow. They also become food for many other animals, such as anteaters, antlions, and chimpanzees.

HUMAN INTERACTION

In some African driver ant species, millions of ants sometimes go on the march together, feeding on any living creature in their path. People get out of the way, but leave their doors and windows open so the ants can clear the mice, flies, and other pests out of their homes!

Friends with the ants

A few ant species have developed a relationship with a completely different species, such as a tree, as a way of getting the food they need. In return, they help that species survive. When two species depend on each other like this, it is called **mutualism**.

Ant farm

It sounds incredible, but some ant colonies actually farm other insects and "milk" them, just as we farm and milk cows. Insects called aphids release honeydew, a sugary liquid, when they feed on plants – and ants love it. To get the honeydew, the ants protect the aphids. They shelter the aphid eggs inside their nests, then take the aphids to their food plants and guard them while they eat. They stroke the aphids with their antennae to make them release the honeydew, and then collect it.

A large carpenter ant stands guard over a cluster of aphids as they feed.

Beware of the ants!

Acacia ants make their home in a bullhorn acacia tree, living inside its hollow thorns. If hungry plant-eaters try to nibble the tree, the ants come out and fight them off, keeping the tree safe. In return, the tree makes little lumps of food called "Beltian bodies" for the ants. The food forms on the leaf tips, where the ants can collect it.

The yellowish blobs on this acacia tree are Beltian bodies.

DID YOU KNOW?

In some ways, ants are surprisingly like humans. They live in large societies, care for their babies, and farm other animals. Ants are also one of the few other species, besides humans, that fight wars against each other.

How do ants have babies?

Ants **reproduce** by laying eggs. Many insects, such as butterflies, lay their eggs, and then fly away. The babies have to look after themselves. But ants, bees, and other social insects look after their young.

An ant colony is like a huge family. There is usually just one queen, who lays all the eggs to make more worker ants. When the queen lays new eggs, workers take them to nursery chambers in the nest, hatch them out, and feed and guard the babies until they become adults.

Ant eggs are all kept together in the safety of the nursery chamber.

HABITAT IN DANGER

The narrow-headed ant is unusual. Some colonies have one egg-laying queen, but others have several. This ant is endangered in the UK, though it's also found in other parts of Europe and Asia. Its delicate habitats are disturbed by farming, logging, quarrying, building, and outdoor sports.

Ant life cycle

An ant goes through various stages on the way to being an adult. This diagram shows the different stages of an ant's life cycle.

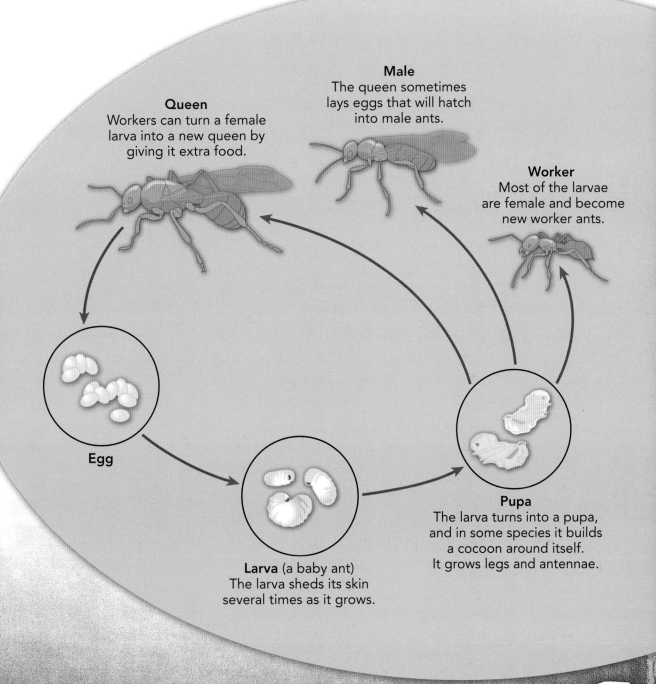

Male
The queen sometimes lays eggs that will hatch into male ants.

Queen
Workers can turn a female larva into a new queen by giving it extra food.

Worker
Most of the larvae are female and become new worker ants.

Egg

Pupa
The larva turns into a pupa, and in some species it builds a cocoon around itself. It grows legs and antennae.

Larva (a baby ant)
The larva sheds its skin several times as it grows.

A queen is born

To make new queens, the workers give some larvae extra food. These larvae grow wings, and become fertile, meaning they can have babies. The new queens leave the nest, and fly around looking for a male ant to mate with. This is called the nuptial flight. Once a queen and a male ant have mated, the male dies, and the queen can start a new colony.

Ant colonies release lots of winged male and female ants at the same time. This means that ants from different colonies can meet and mate.

The queen finds a safe place, sheds her wings, and starts laying eggs. She has to care for the first set of eggs and larvae herself. Once they become adults, they look after her. From now on, the queen sits in her chamber in the nest, sleeps, eats food brought to her by the workers, and lays eggs so that the colony can grow.

How many queens?

Although most ant colonies have one queen, not all do. Some can have many queens at the same time, and a few species have no queen at all. Instead, their female workers can lay eggs when they are needed.

Ant queens usually look like normal ants, but bigger. This is a yellow meadow ant queen, surrounded by much smaller workers.

Did you know?

Some ant queens can live for up to 10 years. Army ant queens lay the most eggs – up to 4 million of them every month!

Bringing up babies

As the queen lays her eggs, worker ants carry them away carefully in their jaws. They take the eggs to a hatching chamber, near the top of the nest, where the Sun's heat can keep them warm. When the white, maggot-like larvae hatch out, the workers carry them to another chamber to be fed and cared for.

Scientists have found that larvae can sway their bodies to and fro to tell the workers that they are hungry. Some species feed their larvae on honeydew from aphids (see page 26), or fungus from a fungus garden (see page 23). Honeypot ants collect food from the living "storage" ants (see page 9) for their larvae. Meat-eating ants catch insect prey and bring it into the nest to feed the young.

A worker black ant carefully moves the colony's larvae by carrying them gently in its jaws.

Some larvae even eat special ant eggs called trophic eggs. Workers can lay these eggs, but they cannot grow into new ants – they are only used as food (just as people use hens' eggs).

Stages of life

Once a larva becomes an adult, it works its way through a series of different jobs. The most dangerous jobs are done by the oldest ants.

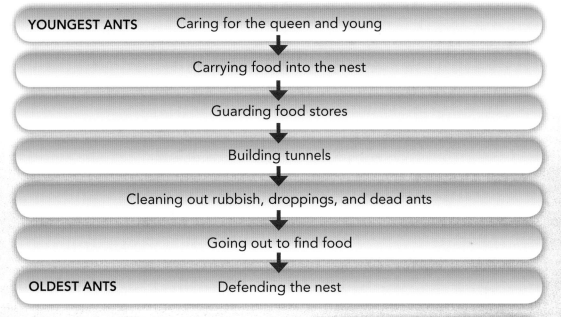

YOUNGEST ANTS   Caring for the queen and young

⬇

Carrying food into the nest

⬇

Guarding food stores

⬇

Building tunnels

⬇

Cleaning out rubbish, droppings, and dead ants

⬇

Going out to find food

⬇

OLDEST ANTS   Defending the nest

HUMAN INTERACTION

In Mexico, Thailand, and other countries, ant eggs and larvae are a popular food. In Mexico, they are known as *escamoles*.

Do other insects live in groups?

Scientists have discovered over a million species of insects. Most of them do not live in large groups, but those that do include most ants, most termites, and some types of bees and wasps.

Wasps

Wasps are closely related to ants. Like ants, they have a sting, a narrow "wasp waist", and biting jaws. The common wasp, or yellowjacket – the type that buzzes around your picnic – lives in a colony, and communicates using chemicals, as ants do. A wasp colony has a queen (sometimes more than one), males, and female workers. The biggest wasp colonies have up to 20,000 wasps in them.

Adult wasps feed on sweet food such as sugar or plant nectar. They also hunt other insects, and collect any other food they can find, to take back to their nest and feed to their larvae.

Common wasps make their nest in a tree, a hole in the ground, or sometimes an old shed or the roof space of a house. They scrape bits of wood from trees, fences, or garden furniture, chew it up, and mix it with their saliva (spit). This makes a papery substance a bit like papier mâché, which they use to build a round nest filled with chambers, or **cells**.

HUMAN INTERACTION

Humans learnt how to make paper from wood by watching wasps chewing wood to make their papery nests.

These wasps are walking across the cells inside their nest, where they keep their eggs and larvae safe.

Bees

Some bees, such as mason bees, live alone. Others, such as bumblebees, live in small colonies of a few hundred. Honeybees have the biggest colonies, with as many as 80,000 members.

Honeybees buzz in and out of flowers, collecting nectar and **pollen** to take back to their nest. There, they look after their queen and feed their larvae. Honeybees build their nests out of beeswax, which they make in their bodies. They use it to make walls of six-sided cells, known as **honeycomb**.

A honeybee gets dusted with flower pollen as it stops to drink the flower's nectar. As it flies around, it spreads the pollen to other flowers.

Beekeepers "farm" bees by giving them hives to build their honeycomb in, and collecting some of their honey.

Bees make honey as a way of storing food. As bees gather nectar, they store it in their stomachs, adding special chemicals that break down food. Then, they bring the nectar back up from their stomachs and put it into cells in their nest. They fan it with their wings to dry it out, making it thick and sticky.

Honeybees use chemical signals, like ants, but also communicate by "dancing". When a worker bee finds a source of food, it moves around inside the nest in a pattern. The speed and angle of the dance tells the other bees how close the food is, and in which direction to find it.

HUMAN INTERACTION

Bees are incredibly important for humans. Besides using their honey, we rely on them to spread pollen from one crop or flower to another. This helps plants to make seeds and fruit.

Meet the termites

Termites live in large colonies, sometimes with over a million members, and feed on plants. A termite colony has a queen, a king, and separate worker and soldier castes.

Some termites dig tunnels in wood, or make nests in trees, but the most amazing termite homes are termite mounds. They can be shaped like round mounds, cones, or tall chimneys or towers. Some termite towers can reach 9 metres (30 feet) tall – as high as a house! Termites build their mounds using mud mixed with saliva. Sometimes they use their own droppings as well.

Unlike ant, bee, and wasp queens, the termite queen has a king to keep her company. He stays beside her in her chamber, and mates with her so that she can keep laying eggs.

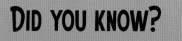

DID YOU KNOW?

Most termites have no eyes.

The king is only slightly bigger than a worker, but a termite queen can be enormous. Her abdomen grows into a huge, soft, sausage shape, so big that she can't move. The biggest termite queens can reach 10 centimetres (4 inches) long, and more than 2 centimetres (0.8 inches) wide.

HUMAN INTERACTION

Some species of termite cause problems for humans by damaging crops, including tea and sugarcane. Others nest under wooden houses and chew at the timber. Sometimes they even make houses collapse.

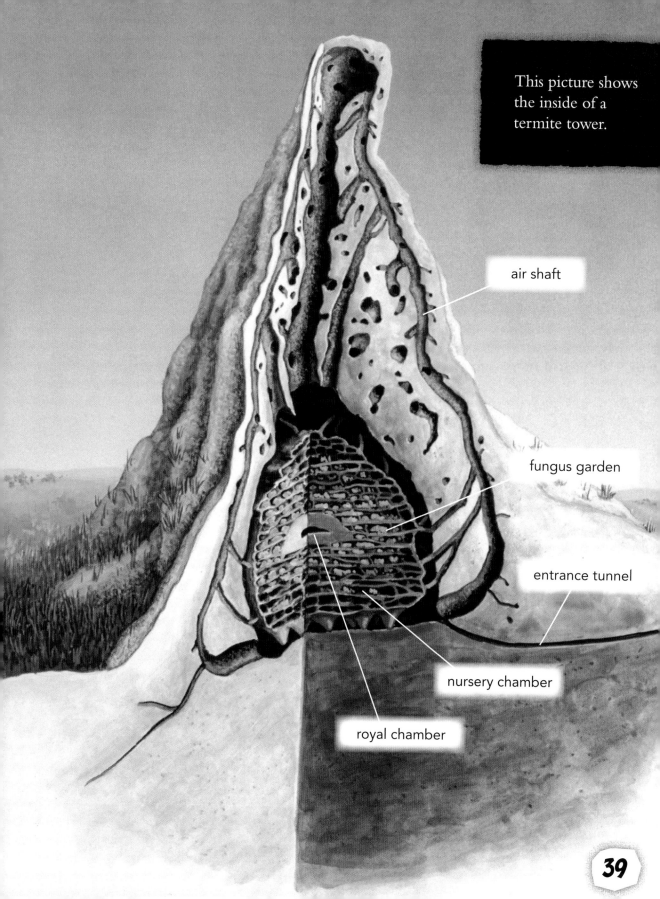

This picture shows the inside of a termite tower.

air shaft

fungus garden

entrance tunnel

nursery chamber

royal chamber

What can we learn from ants?

When you think of an intelligent animal, you might think of a chimpanzee or a dolphin – probably not a tiny creepy-crawly. Yet when social insects work together in a colony, they can do amazing things. Ants, along with other social insects such as bees, wasps, and termites, are incredibly good at sending messages, building structures, and running a society.

HABITAT IN DANGER

Ants and other social insects are usually very good at surviving. There are large numbers of them, and most species are not endangered. But some do suffer from habitat loss, when humans take over wild land to build cities, farms, and roads. This could get worse over time, as the human population grows. We need to find ways to live alongside insects, protecting them as well as our crops and homes.

Science challenge

Scientists still don't understand all the secrets of social insects. There are many questions to answer, and unknown species to discover. Studying ants, bees, wasps, or termites is an exciting area of science to work in. It can also be useful, because we can learn from the way social insects do things.

Scientists who design robots have been inspired by ants. They have developed small, simple robots that can signal to each other and work in a team, as ants do. Teams of ant robots are good at things such as exploring land surfaces and finding routes. They could be used to do dangerous tasks, such as searching for **landmines** or exploring other planets.

This large, real ant is investigating a robot ant named Alice. Scientists in Switzerland built Alice to try to find out more about ant behaviour.

Fact file

Ants

Body: Slim, with a hard, smooth exoskeleton, and narrow waist

Vision: Two large compound eyes and three ocelli, although some species are blind

Antennae: Elbowed (bent) in the middle

Mouthparts: Slicing and chewing jaws

Wings: Queens and males have two pairs of wings until they have mated

Size of worker: 1–30 millimetres (0.04–1.18 inches) long

Size of male: 1.5–30 millimetres (0.06–1.18 inches) long

Size of queen: 2–50 millimetres (0.08–2 inches) long

Maximum colony size: Over 20 million (army ants)

Food: Insects, other animals, plants, fungus, or honeydew

Type of home: Nest in soil, wood, trees, or other plants

Common wasps

Body: Tough exoskeleton, striped abdomen, and narrow waist

Eyes: Two large compound eyes and three ocelli

Antennae: Bent, with a short, thick base and longer end section

Mouthparts: Scraping, slicing, and chewing jaws

Wings: Two pairs of wings

Size of worker: 12–15 millimetres (0.5–0.6 inches) long

Size of male: 16–17 millimetres (0.6–0.7 inches) long

Size of queen: About 20 millimetres (0.8 inches) long

Maximum colony size: Around 20,000

Food: Plant nectar, sugary foods, insects, and meat

Type of home: Papery nest made from chewed up wood

Ants live almost everywhere on Earth. This map shows where three types of ant can be found: honey pot ants, leafcutter ants, and weaver ants.

BEES

Body: Thicker, hairy body

Eyes: Two large compound eyes and three ocelli

Antennae: Bent, with a short, thick base and longer end section

Mouthparts: Straw-like sucking mouth called a proboscis

Wings: Two pairs of wings

Maximum colony size: Around 80,000

Food: Plant nectar and pollen

Type of home: Nest made from honeycomb, or a human-made beehive

TERMITES

Body: Soft, pale body

Eyes: Usually blind and eyeless

Antennae: Short and bobbled, like a row of beads

Wings: Queens and males have two pairs of wings until they have mated

Mouthparts: Chewing jaws

Maximum colony size: About 2 million

Food: Cellulose (tough plant substance)

Type of home: Nest in wood or a tree, or build a termite mound

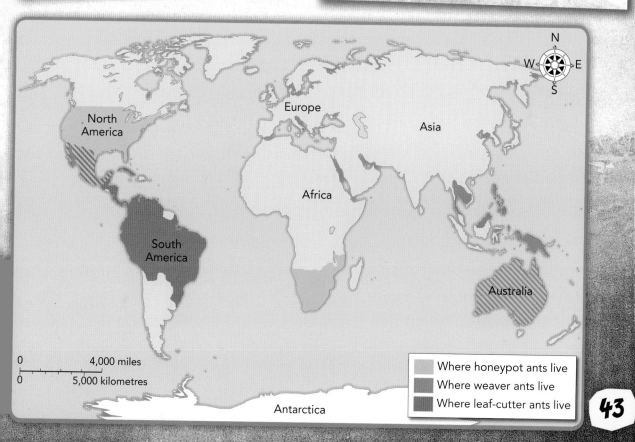

North America

Europe

Asia

Africa

South America

Australia

Antarctica

0   4,000 miles
0   5,000 kilometres

Where honeypot ants live
Where weaver ants live
Where leaf-cutter ants live

Glossary

abdomen third and usually largest of an insect's three body sections

antenna (more than one: **antennae**) sense organs or feelers on an insect's head

caste particular type of ant or other social insect within a colony

cell small chamber in a bee or wasp nest

chemical pure substance. A chemical can be a solid, liquid, or a gas.

colony group of social insects living together

compound eye eye made up of many small sections

ecosystem living and non-living things in a particular area

endangered at risk of dying out

exoskeleton hard covering on the outside of the body

fungus (more than one: **fungi**) type of living thing. A mushroom is an example of a fungus.

habitat natural home or surroundings of a living thing

honeycomb structure made by bees for storing honey

honeydew sugary substance from plants, released by aphids as they feed

landmine small bomb buried just below the surface of the ground, which can explode when stepped on

larva (more than one: **larvae**) baby insect

mandible insect jaw

mate when a male and female come together to produce young

mutualism when two species depend on each other and help each other to survive

nectar sweet substance made by flowers

nomadic moving from place to place without a fixed home

nutrient substance in food that living things need in order to grow and live

ocellus (more than one: **ocelli**) type of small, simple eye

organism living thing

pheromone chemical used to send scent messages

pollen cells released by flowers for making seeds

prey animal that is hunted and eaten by another animal

pupa (more than one: **pupae**) stage of an insect's life between larva and adult

reproduce to have babies or young

species particular type of living thing

Find out more

Books

Ants (Animal Lives), Sally Morgan (QED Publishing, 2009)
Army Ants (Animal Scavengers), Sandra Markle (Lerner Books, 2010)
Bugs (Wildlife Watchers), Terry Jennings (QED Publishing, 2011)
Insects (1000 Facts), Belinda Gallagher (Miles Kelly Publishing, 2007)
Minibeasts in the Soil (Where to Find Minibeasts), Sarah Ridley
    (Franklin Watts, 2010)

Websites

www.nhm.ac.uk/kids-only/naturecams/antcam
Have a look at the leafcutter ants on the Natural History
Museum's antcam!

www.bbc.co.uk/nature/life/Ant
Find out more about ants and watch some great videos on the
BBC website.

www.antblog.co.uk/keepingants/kids
Find out how to keep and watch ants at home.

DVDs

Life in the Undergrowth, David Attenborough (BBC, 2005)
Microcosmos, Claude Nuridsany and Jean-Marc Perennou
    (Fox, 1996; remastered 2008)
Richard Hammond's Invisible Worlds (BBC, 2010)

Places to visit

BUGS at London Zoo
Outer Circle, Regent's Park
London NW1 4RY
www.zsl.org/zsl-london-zoo/exhibits/bugs

Bug World
Bristol Zoo Gardens
Clifton, Bristol BS8 3HA
www.bristolzoo.org.uk/bug-world

Edinburgh Butterfly and Insect World
Dobbies Garden World, Melville Nursery
Midlothian Scotland EH18 1AZ
www.edinburgh-butterfly-world.co.uk

More topics to research

Which parts of this book did you find the most interesting? What subjects would you like to know more about?

- Do you like the idea of building your own ant farm, or getting a really good close-up look at ants? Some of the websites listed show you how to capture and look after some ants so that you can watch how they live. You could trap one ant carefully in a glass jar or other clear container, and use a strong magnifying glass or a USB handheld microscope to look at it.

- Lots of people keep bees as a hobby. Some garden centres, museums, city farms, and zoos also have real bees in hives. If you'd like to see beekeeping and beehives in real life, or learn about how to keep bees, look up local beekeeping organizations and wildlife centres to find places where the public can visit and watch bees and beekeepers.

- If you're interested in computers and robots, try researching ant robotics. Look for books on robotics, and find out which universities are building and testing robot ants. Are there other types of insect robots? How do robot insects work? Are they different from other robots?

Index